Beautiful NAILS

DEBORAH A. MACK
Nail Designer and Contributing Writer

BIANCA SIMBALL
Technical Assistant and Adviser

C. DIANE RYNER
Associate Writer

Publications International, Ltd.

Louis Weber, C.E.O.
Publications International, Ltd.
7373 North Cicero Avenue
Lincolnwood, Illinois 60646

Manufactured in U.S.A.

8 7 6 5 4 3 2 1

ISBN 1-56173-733-X

Contributing writer **Deborah A. Mack** is Director of Nail Education and teaches Advanced Nail and Reflexology for Pivot Point Beauty School in Chicago, Illinois. As a certified nail technician and educator, she has been featured in numerous publications including *Nails* magazine, and she is a member of the National Nail Technicians Group Ltd.

Bianca Simball is a licensed cosmetologist and nail technician and is the Director of Graduate Education for Pivot Point International, Inc.

C. Diane Ryner is a public relations writer for Pivot Point International, Inc.

Photography by Sam Griffith Studios.
Cover backgound photo by Siede-Preis Photography.

Royal Model Management models: Colleen Collins, Cindy Cottrell, Phyllis Gooden, and Kevin Lingle.

CONTENTS

INTRODUCTION

Men and women have been designing for and caring for hands and nails since as far back as 15,000 B.C. In northern Turkey archaeologists have found abrasive-backed shells that most likely served as the first nail files. Written histories and religious writings from the time of Alexander the Great refer to the grooming of the hands and nails. And in ancient China long, gold-plated nails were symbols of obvious status.

During the late 19th century a French chemist developed a loose powder meant to make the nails shiny. This was the beginning of the modern-day practice of polishing the nails. Today nail polishes come in a spectrum of colors that was unimaginable then, from the palest of pinks to the brightest of reds.

Well-manicured nails are not merely decorative; they signify good personal hygiene. Today both men and women sport carefully groomed nails.

This book offers you step-by-step directions for practicing various nail procedures at home. By following the simple steps, you will be able to create all the looks shown here, from the basic manicure to more intricate nail art.

How your hands look contributes to your total look. With good nail grooming, you will look better and feel better. Get started today!

OVERVIEW OF TECHNIQUES

Manicure Techniques

The basic plain manicure shown on pages 17–21 keeps nails in a healthy condition with minimum required maintenance time. This simple technique can make even the shortest nails look well groomed and well kept up. It's ideal for both women and men.

The basic manicure gives you a strong foundation on which to build more advanced techniques. The French manicure, for example, exaggerates the look of the nail's natural state. It takes a little practice to master, but once you have learned it you can wear it for almost any occasion. Its classic design suits it for casual or elegant events. A dramatic variation of the French manicure is called the chevron. By simply changing the shape of the design on the nail's tip, you create a new, exciting look.

Just as important as the manicure for the hands is the pedicure for your feet. Because your feet act as the workhorses of your body, carrying your weight all day, they need special attention. Often, however, they are the most neglected part of the body. When's the last time you thought about your feet longer than to decide which pair of shoes to wear?

Artificial tips and silk wrap are two excellent ways to enhance nails that are less than perfect. Silk wrapping strengthens, repairs, and protects your natural nail. Putting on nail tips adds immediate length to your nails. By improving the nail plate on which you are working, this extra strength or length can give your nails a dramatic new flair.

Nail art is a great opportunity to use your artistic skills and let your imagination run free. Your nails are your canvas, on which you are free to paint without limitations. Let your personal style shine through in the pictures you create.

Color Selection

A flattering shade of polish can enhance your hands, but a poor choice can detract from your total look. Skin tone plays an important part in determining which shade of polish is most attractive on you. You can determine shades of polish that complement your skin color by studying the categories in the charts that follow. Find the category that best describes both your hair and eye color. Once you find that category, look for your skin tone. Across from your skin tone you will find the polish shades that look best with your skin's color. Although these are the colors that complement your skin tone the best, most people can wear almost any color. When experimenting with other colors, pay attention to shades and intensity.

CATEGORY A

Hair color: Golden brown, chestnut brown, black-brown, black, gray

Eye color: Dark brown, gray, black, dark blue, dark green

Skin tone	*Polish shade*
White	Roses, pinks, reds, blue-reds
Light to dark rose-beige	Wines, burgundies
Olive	True reds, blue-reds
Black	Burgundies and vivid colors

Avoid warm tones such as oranges, corals, and yellows.

CATEGORY B

Hair color: Light to medium ash blonde, light to medium ash brown, gray

Eye color: Clear blue to gray-blue, clear green to gray-green, hazel, soft brown

Skin tone	*Polish shade*
Fair with pink tone	Pinks, plums
Light to deep rose-beige	Roses, wines, burgundies

Avoid yellow tones such as peaches and oranges.

CATEGORY C

Hair color: Golden blonde, strawberry blonde, light to dark golden brown, gray

Eye color: Light to dark blue, blue-gray, light golden brown, blue-green, golden green

Skin tone	*Polish shade*
Pale to golden ivory	Peaches, corals
Light to medium beige	Poppy reds, orange-reds

Avoid dark tones such as deep oranges.

....

CATEGORY D

Hair color: Bright red to deep auburn, honey blonde, light to dark brown, deep chestnut brown, gray

Eye color: Light to dark brown, brown, golden green, hazel

Skin tone	*Polish shade*
Ivory	Peach shades
Light, medium, or dark beige	Orange-reds

Avoid dark tones such as brown or rust shades.

Nail Anatomy

Before you start your manicure, take time to learn a little about the structure of the fingernail. This knowledge will tell you why certain procedures are important in caring for your nails.

The **nail plate** is the fingernail itself. It is made up of dead skin cells called keratin, which are held together by a tightly adhering protein glue. The nail plate grows forward from the cuticle to protect the tips of the fingers and toes.

The **free edge** is the portion of the nail plate that extends beyond the fingertip.

The **nail bed** is the soft tissue directly beneath your fingernail (nail plate). It is made of a special slippery skin that allows the nail plate to slide forward as it grows out. A healthy nail bed is usually pink in color, because of the blood vessels that nourish it.

The **nail grooves** are the areas on each side of the nail plate where the sides of the nail meet the surrounding skin. They allow the nail to slide smoothly as it is pushed forward during growth.

The **matrix** is the heart of nail growth. It lies underneath the skin above the first knuckle and contains the lymph glands, nerves, and blood vessels from which the nail is formed. Because the nail is formed here, it is very important not to damage this delicate center of production. Damage to the matrix can cause permanently deformed nails.

The **cuticle** is the skin that covers and protects the matrix from damage. It forms a watertight seal to prevent bacteria and germs from entering the sensitive matrix area. Because this seal is essential to insure against infection of the matrix, the cuticle should never be cut or otherwise removed.

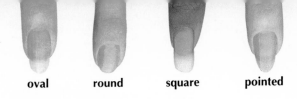

oval   round   square   pointed

Hangnails are folds of skin that have separated from the finger, leaving an open area where bacteria can enter. Dry skin can increase the likelihood of developing hangnails.

Nail Shapes

Nails can be filed into four basic nail shapes: oval, round, square, or pointed. The shape you choose depends on the shape and size of your fingers as well as personal preference.

The most common shape is the oval, which requires some length. This classic shape makes the fingers appear more slender.

The round shape is commonly used on shorter nails. Long, thin fingers appear shorter when nails are filed into this shape.

The sporty, square-shaped nail, which gives a dramatic look to any finger shape, is quickly increasing in popularity. Besides looking good for all occasions, it helps to maintain the nail's strength.

Strong nails are required for the pointed shape, because the supporting sides are filed away. However, this shape is great for lengthening short, stubby fingers.

Hints and Tips

Never shake your nail polish. To prevent air bubbles from forming on the nail, roll the bottle gently between your hands.

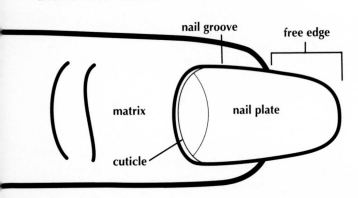

nail groove   free edge

matrix   nail plate

cuticle

Keep your cuticles in top condition by liberally applying lotion to your hands and wearing cotton gloves to bed at night.

Avoid infection by applying an antiseptic lotion or spray after trimming hangnails.

For away-from-home nail repairs, always carry an emergency kit consisting of an emery board, glue, silk or linen, a clear top coat, and a small bottle of polish remover.

If polish has become old and thick, an enamel thinner can be added. Just a few drops mixed thoroughly into the old polish will once again make it easy to apply.

If your polish becomes nicked or smudged, you can easily repair it without having to redo the entire nail.

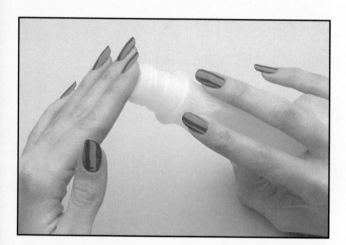

Simply dip the pad of another finger (not the finger with the damage) into polish remover.

Gently wipe over the smudge until it is smoothed away.

Basic Sanitation Procedures

Before working on your nails, it is important to wash your hands in warm, soapy water to prevent the spreading of germs. To further ensure against infection, use an antiseptic spray or foam after washing.

Since hangnails are essentially a break in the skin, they produce a portal of entry for germs and bacteria. To help prevent hangnails, you should keep your hands moisturized by applying lotion regularly. If you do get a hangnail, it should be trimmed with cuticle nippers to stop it from growing any larger. Cut the hangnail down to the skin's surface, but do not cut any tissue still attached to the finger. To reduce your chances of infection, apply a topical antiseptic ointment directly to the hangnail area after trimming.

Emery boards and orangewood sticks should not be shared with others. They are meant to be disposable in order to prevent the spreading of germs from one person to another.

Metal and plastic tools are reusable and can be shared with others. However, they should be washed in warm, soapy water and sanitized in a disinfectant before each use. Nail files with a foam center can also be washed and sanitized for use on more than one person.

Tools and Implements

All the tools and implements you need for the projects in this book are described here. With each procedure you'll find a list of all the materials needed for that technique. Collect all these items before you start so that you can move smoothly through each step without having to stop and look for missing items.

Emery boards are files for natural nail care. They have two different textures (grits), one on each side. The coarseness of the grit determines how powerful the action of the file is.

Nail files are for heavier filing purposes, such as for use on nails with silk and plastic tips. They also come in different grits as well as a variety of shapes and colors.

Three-way buffers have two different grits on one side (black and white) and a smooth, gray material on the other side. The smooth side is used to bring a glossy shine to nails when polish is not desired, such as for men's manicures.

Block buffers are rectangular buffers with foam centers used for finer buffing. Usually they have two grits—two sides are a heavy grit and two sides are a fine grit.

Orangewood sticks are wooden manicure sticks with a variety of uses, such as cleaning underneath the nail, removing polish from around the cuticle, pushing back the cuticle, and applying nail-art products.

Cotton can be wrapped around an orangewood stick for cleaning under the free edge. It is also used to remove lotion and old polish from the nail plate.

Manicure sticks are disposable sticks that are prewrapped with cotton and shaped to a point.

Finger bowls are plastic, metal, or glass bowls filled with liquids used for the soaking stage of a manicure.

Nailbrushes are small plastic brushes used to cleanse the hands and nails of debris and lotions.

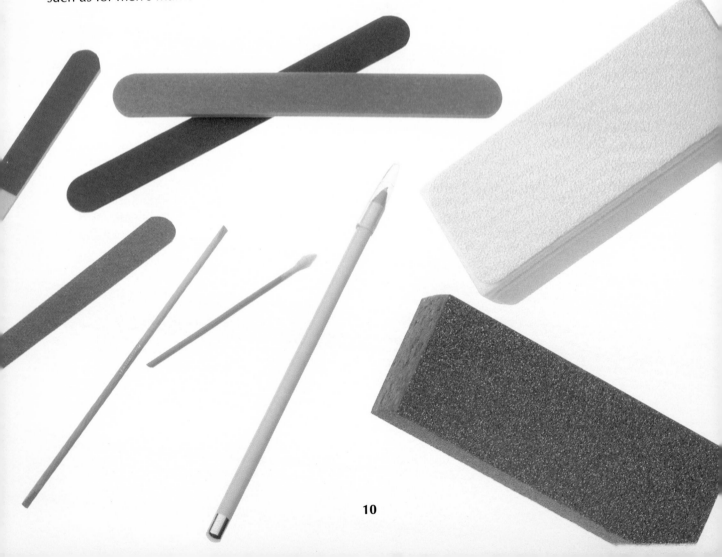

Nail clippers are metal devices used to cut or shorten the fingernails and toenails.

Cuticle nippers are metal devices used to trim hangnails and cut nail-art materials.

A **white stick** is a pencil used to whiten underneath the nail's free edge.

Manicure scissors are used to cut silk, linen, and nail-art products.

Tweezers are metal pincers used to pick up small items.

A **foot bath** is a large container used to keep water warm for soaking the feet during a pedicure.

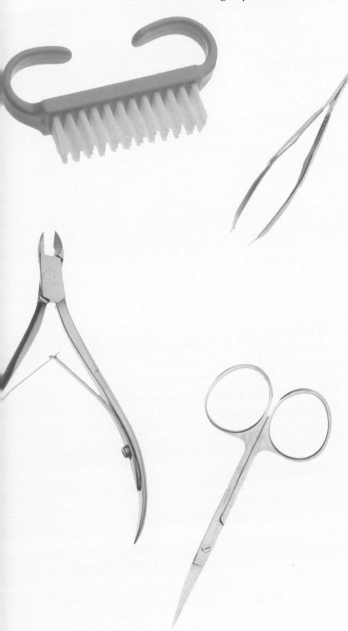

Foot files are large plastic files used to remove calluses from the feet.

Pumice stones are stones made of volcanic ash with an abrasive texture used to exfoliate dry skin from the feet.

Slippers are paper or plastic foot coverings used to protect the feet at the end of a pedicure.

Toe separators are foam plastic devices used to keep the toes separated during polishing to prevent the polish from smudging.

Hot-oil manicure machines are electrical heating units used to warm the creme for hot-oil manicures. They come with disposable plastic cups, which eliminate messy cleanups.

Acrylic paintbrushes come in a variety of sizes and are used to apply acrylic paint in nail-art designs.

Table mats and towels cover your work area to prevent damage to your tabletop from spills or leaks.

Nail Products

Polish remover comes in two types, acetone and nonacetone. Both remove nail enamel from the nail plate. Acetone is used on natural nails; nonacetone is usually used on silk-wrapped nails and nail tips because it doesn't damage the product.

A **nail correcting pen** is a special felt-tip pen filled with polish remover for spot corrections. The felt tip can be removed to refill the pen.

Cuticle oil is a gentle oil sometimes made with an almond base that is brushed on and massaged into the cuticle area and surrounding skin.

Massage creme is used to prevent friction burns during a massage and to soften and moisturize the skin.

Hand antiseptic comes in spray, foam, and creme forms. It is used to reduce bacteria, viruses, and funguses on the skin.

Nail glue is used to adhere tips, silk, and some nail-art items to the nail plate. It comes in different degrees of viscosity (thickness). This viscosity determines drying time—the thicker the glue the slower it dries.

Silks and linens are fabrics applied to the natural nail plate to add strength. They are also used in nail mending.

Adhesive tabs are glue-based tabs used to attach press-on nails to the natural nail plate.

Polishes and enamels are brush-on products used to coat the natural nail plate. They fall into four basic categories:

> **Base coats** are applied directly to the natural nail to protect it against stains from the pigments in colored polishes.

> **Ridge fillers** are thicker base coats used to even out ridges or bumps on the natural nail.

> **Color enamels** are applied twice over the base coat to give strength and color to the nail plate.

> **Top coats** are applied last over the color enamels to keep them from peeling or chipping.

Quick-dry is an oil product sprayed or brushed over the top coat to quicken the drying process.

Acrylic paints are pigments used to draw designs on the nail.

Plastic nail tips are pieces of nail-shaped plastic used to elongate the nail.

Press-on nails are plastic nail shapes applied over the entire natural nail.

Sloughing lotion is a creme massaged into the feet to exfoliate dead skin cells.

Foot powder is applied to the feet to deodorize and reduce the chance of blisters caused by friction on the feet from tight shoes.

Foot antiseptic spray is used to reduce bacteria, viruses, and funguses on the foot.

Antimicrobial soap is a cleaning solution used to reduce bacteria, viruses, and funguses on the skin and to cleanse the skin and nail area.

Rhinestones are small, shiny appliqués used in nail art.

Decals come in many types of designs and are sized and shaped especially for nail art.

Striping tape is an adhesive-backed tape that comes in a variety of colors and is used for nail-art designing.

Nail charms are appliqués that are usually gold-filled and come in various styles and are attached to the natural nail plate.

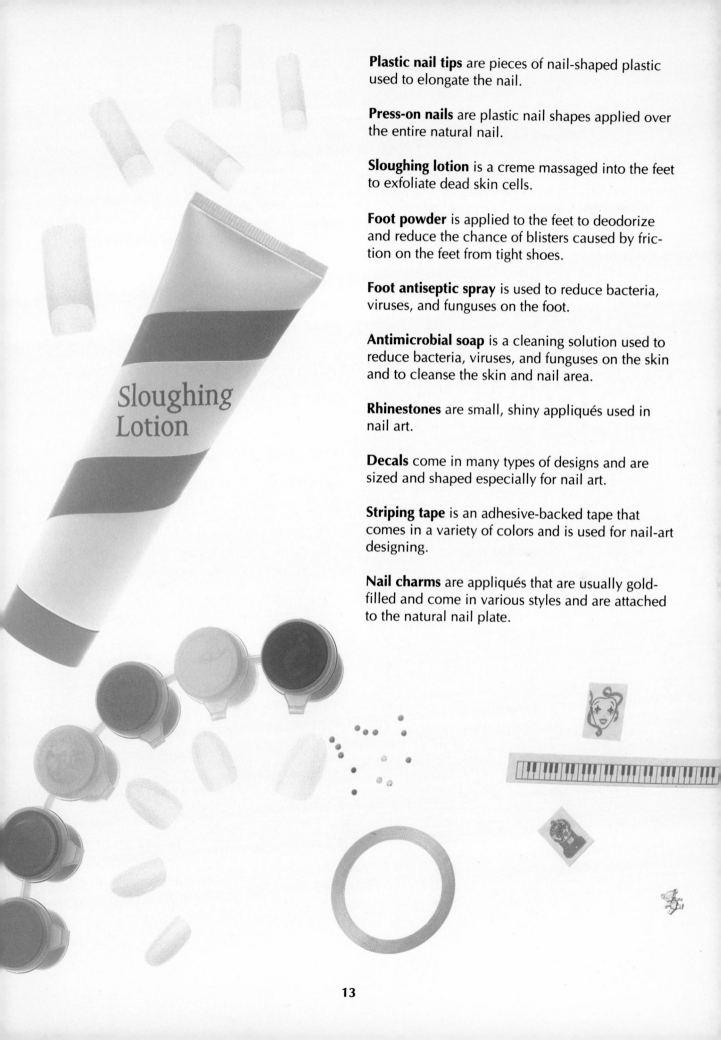

MASSAGE

The massage is the relaxing part of the manicure and pedicure procedures. For a manicure, begin massaging at the elbow and work your way down to the fingertips. For a pedicure, begin at the shin area and continue down to the tips of the toes.

Because many of the body's reflex points are located on the hands and feet, the massaging techniques send a message to the brain to release the body's natural pain killers called endorphins. The release of the endorphins creates an all-over sensation of well-being.

Creme is used during the massage to moisturize and soften the hands and feet. It also reduces friction to avoid painful pulling and burning of the skin.

HAND MASSAGE

MATERIALS NEEDED:

Massage creme or nongreasy oil

1

Remove watch and all jewelry before beginning the massage procedure. Briskly rub massage creme or nongreasy oil between your hands to warm it before applying to the skin. Starting at the elbow, apply the creme liberally and work down to the fingertips, saturating all exposed skin.

2

Use the Indian burn technique to massage the forearm. Grasp the top of the forearm with your elbows extended outward. Twist, moving your hands in opposite directions. Make sure you use enough creme to avoid painful friction burns.

3

Place the elbow on the tabletop. Support the wrist with one hand, and with the other slowly rotate the wrist three times in each direction to relax and loosen muscle tension.

4

Further massage the wrist by placing your thumbs on each side of the wrist bone. Slide your fingers back and forth to increase circulation.

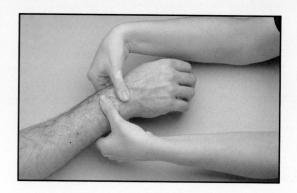

5

This sponging technique is like kneading bread. Place your hands on the top of the hand with your thumbs covering the wrist. Now squeeze your hands together while pulling toward the outside of the hand.

6

Use a pulling technique to slide the thumb through your hand. When you reach the tip, rotate the tip three times in each direction. Finish by using the pull/slide technique once more. Follow the same procedure with each finger.

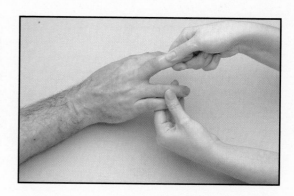

FOOT MASSAGE

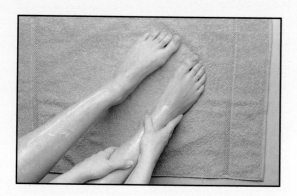

MATERIALS NEEDED:

Massage creme or nongreasy oil

1

Briskly rub massage creme or nongreasy oil between your hands to warm it. Liberally apply the creme from the area directly below the knee to the tips of the toes. Make sure all the skin is saturated.

2

Use the Indian burn technique to massage the shin area. Place your hands on the shin with your elbows extended outward. Twist, moving your hands in opposite directions. Make sure you use enough lotion to avoid painful friction burns.

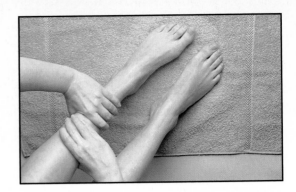

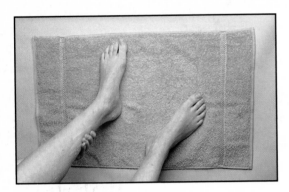

3

Starting at the back of the shin, slide your fingers downward toward the heel while squeezing the muscles in that area. This massages the powerful Achilles tendon.

4

With your elbows extended, place your thumbs on top of the foot at the ankle area. Slide your thumbs in opposite directions back and forth across the ankle.

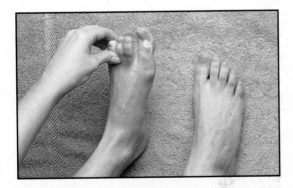

5

Two pulling techniques can be used to massage the toes. For the first technique, position your thumb on top of the toe and your forefinger underneath the toe. Pull the toe through your fingers. The second technique is the same, except position your thumb on one side of the toe and your fingers on the other side and pull the toe.

6

The thumbs are used to massage the sole of the foot. Starting at the heel, place your thumbs one on top of the other, with your elbows extended. Apply downward pressure as thumbs walk from the heel to the ball of the foot. Then reverse the steps and walk your thumbs from the ball of the foot to the heel.

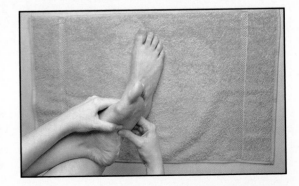

BASIC MANICURE

The basic manicure is the first step in learning good grooming habits for your nails. To keep your nails looking healthy and cared for, it is important to give yourself a manicure once a week—every week. The basic procedure takes less than half an hour, so it fits easily into even the busiest schedules.

This easy procedure can quickly be mastered by anyone with a little practice. And once you have perfected it, you can vary your polish techniques to create many new and interesting nail designs.

This manicure is perfect for any nail length and especially benefits nail biters. The better the nails look, the less a nail biter will want to bite them.

MATERIALS NEEDED:

Soap	Nailbrush
Cotton	Towel
Nail polish remover	Hand creme
Orangewood stick or manicure stick	Hand antiseptic
	Base coat
Emery board	Color polish
Cuticle oil	Top coat
Finger bowl	Quick-dry

1

Before starting any nail procedure, gather all tools and products you will be using. To help prevent infections, you must wash your hands with soap and warm water before working on your nails.

2

To remove old nail polish quickly, saturate a cotton ball in polish remover and place it over your nail plate for ten seconds. Then pull the cotton toward the free edge to prevent polish from getting on the cuticle. To remove polish from the hard-to-reach nail grooves, dip a cotton-tipped manicure stick into polish remover. Work around the groove with the cotton-covered tip.

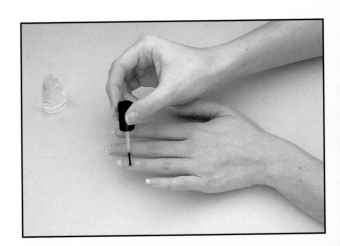

3

File the nails to the desired length and shape. Always file the nails from corner to center. To achieve the oval shape, round only the corners of the nails, leaving the top of the free edge straight.

4

Brush cuticle oil onto the skin surrounding the entire nail. Gently massage the oil into the skin to soften.

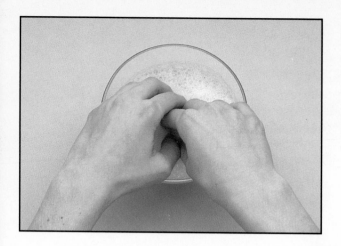

5

Place your hands in a finger bowl filled with warm, soapy water and allow them to soak for 5 minutes.

6

Use a nailbrush to cleanse and exfoliate the skin. Always brush away from yourself to avoid splashing your clothes. After the soaking step, dry hands with a clean towel. It is important to dry hands completely to prevent chapping.

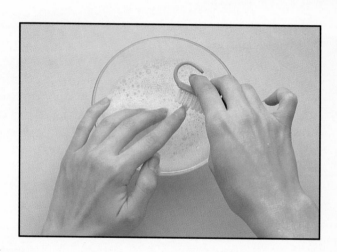

7

Using a cotton-tipped manicure stick or an orangewood stick wrapped in cotton, gently push back the cuticles. Since the cuticle covers the sensitive matrix area, be especially cautious when working in this area. Massage a liberal amount of hand creme thoroughly into your hands and fingers.

8

Spray or soak a cotton ball with hand antiseptic and place the cotton on the nail plate. Pull it over the nail edge to remove the excess lotion from the nail plate. Pay extra attention to this step, because nail polish will not stick properly to the nail plate if any lotion remains on it.

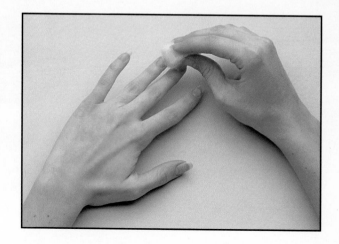

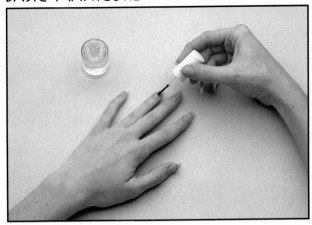

9

Polishing the nails keeps them strong and helps them to grow longer. A base coat protects your nails against stains from color polishes. Like polish, it is applied to the entire nail in 3 easy strokes, as described in steps 10 through 12. Start with the little finger and work toward the thumb.

10

To apply the color polish, dip your brush in the polish to get the necessary amount of polish for your nail length. The longer your nails are, the more polish you will need. Place the polish brush just above the cuticle at a 45-degree angle and gently pull the brush toward the free edge, evenly distributing the color.

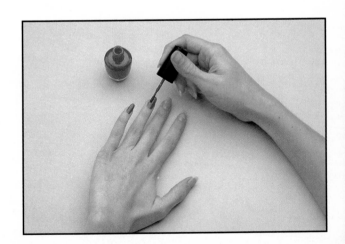

11

Gently pull your skin away from the right nail groove. Starting at the right of your first stroke just above the cuticle, apply the second stroke of polish.

12

Check the amount of polish remaining on your brush and add more if necessary. Then repeat step 11 on the left side of the nail plate. To remove polish from your cuticle or the surrounding skin area, use either a cotton-wrapped orangewood stick dipped in nail polish remover or a nail polish correcting pen. Apply a second coat in the same manner.

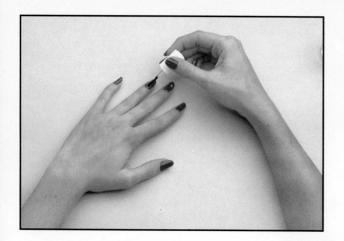

13

A clear top coat over the color polish helps protect the color polish and adds a high-gloss shine. Apply the top coat using the same 3-stroke process.

14

To seal in the color polish and prevent chipping, apply the top coat to the tip of the free edge. Turn your hand over and carefully polish the underside of the nail also. This will help strengthen your nails. Applying top coat periodically between manicures will preserve the look of your polished nails.

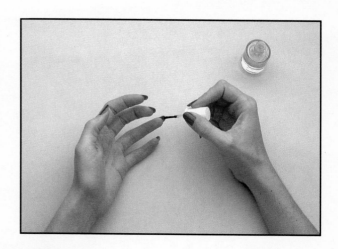

15

To speed up drying time of the top coat, apply quick-dry. It comes in both brush-on and spray forms. The brush-on is applied to the nail in the same way that polish is applied. Hold the spray bottle at least 6 inches away to prevent the pressure of the spray from damaging your polish. Spray evenly over your nails. It will still take $2\frac{1}{2}$ hours for the 4 coats of polish to dry completely.

FRENCH MANICURE

This elegant, classic style simply exaggerates the look of your natural nail, making it the perfect accessory to any fashion wear. The look is achieved by applying white polish in a half-moon shape on the nail's free edge and then polishing over the entire nail with a pale pink, peach, or beige enamel.

MATERIALS NEEDED:

All items from the basic
  manicure, page 17
Stark white polish
Soft or opaque pink polish

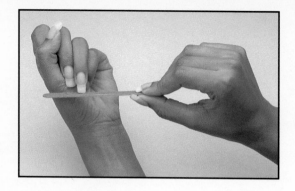

1

The dramatic square nail shape is ideal for the French manicure. To achieve this look, file the free edge straight across. Do not round off the corners. To define and sharpen the square look, file the sides of the nail along the nail groove to form a 90-degree angle. Perform steps 1 through 9 from the basic manicure, pages 18–20.

2

With white polish, outline a crescent moon shape, starting where the pink nail bed meets the white free edge.

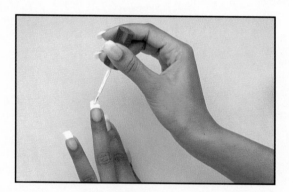

3

Using outward strokes, fill in the rest of the free edge with the white polish.

4

Because stark white polish takes longer to dry, wait several minutes before applying more polish. Using the 3-stroke polishing method, apply 2 coats of soft or opaque pink over the entire nail plate.

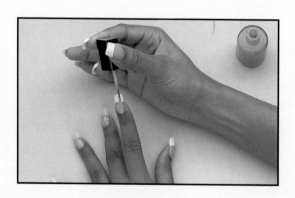

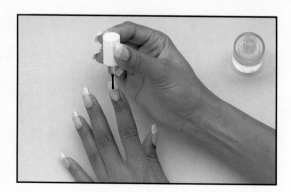

5

Apply top coat to the nail plate, tip, and underside of each nail to seal your French manicure. Finish the procedure by applying quick-dry.

CHEVRON FRENCH MANICURE

The chevron is a variation of the traditional French manicure. It is essentially the same as the French manicure except the shape of the white polish on the nail tips is an upside-down V shape instead of a half-moon oval. Although the change is subtle, the new mood it can create is great. People will stop to look at your interesting design.

MATERIALS NEEDED:

All items from the basic manicure, page 17, and French manicure, page 22

1

Perform steps 1 through 9 from the basic manicure, pages 18–20. Starting at the left side of the nail where the pink nail bed meets the free edge, use stark white polish to draw a straight diagonal line to the opposite corner of the nail. Repeat the procedure on the right side of the nail. Using outward strokes, fill in the rest of the free edge with stark white polish to create an inverted V shape.

2

Using the 3-stroke polishing method, apply two coats of soft or opaque pink to the entire nail plate.

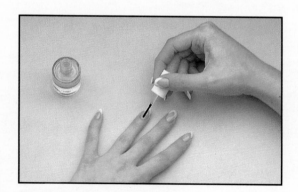

3

Apply top coat to the nail plate, tip, and underside of each nail to seal your chevron manicure. Finish the procedure by applying quick-dry.

FRENCH TWISTS

The French manicure has unlimited variations. By simply changing the polish colors, you can create a completely new look. Soft white or beige can be substituted on the tip to lessen the dramatic effect of the stark white. Likewise, peach and sheer blue can be substituted for the pale pink more commonly used on the nail bed.

For a more subtle look, substitute soft white for the stark white on the free edge.

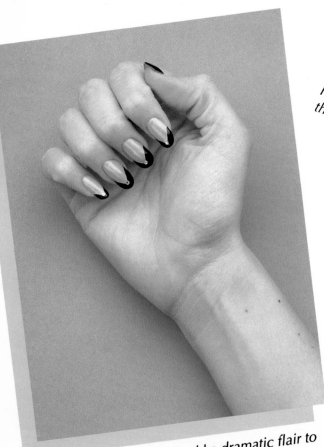

Classic black and white add a dramatic flair to the traditional French manicure. First, apply two coats of opalescent white polish over your base coat. Then, to create the black tip, follow the same steps used in the chevron technique (page 25), but use black instead of white polish on the free edge.

Using bold colors will draw attention to your design variation. For example, the reversed French manicure substitutes black polish for the white tip, and the natural nail plate is painted frosted white. For special occasions, metallic golds, silvers, and coppers can add a touch of sophistication to your finished look. Paint the nail plate a festive color to match your outfit, and then polish the nail tip with your complementary metallic choice. This will add the perfect finishing touch for an elegant evening out. Or add sparkle by including rhinestones in your finished design.

MAN'S MANICURE

Many men often neglect the condition of their nails. The smallest details, however, can make or break the effect of a man's total look. It's just as essential for men to keep up their nails as it is for women. The man's manicure follows the same steps as the basic manicure except that the nails are not polished with enamel but are buffed to a high shine.

Everyone loves to be pampered, and men are no exception. Give the men in your life a personal gift they'll appreciate. Your father, brother, or friend will not only benefit from the relaxing and moisturizing effects of the massage but will love the look of nicely manicured nails.

MATERIALS NEEDED:

Soap	Orangewood stick
Emery board	Hand creme
Cuticle oil	Cotton
Finger bowl	3-way buffer
Nailbrush	White stick
Towel	

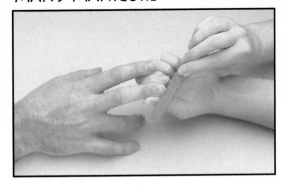

1

File the nails to shape them and remove rough edges. Perform steps 1 through 8 from the basic manicure, pages 18–19.

2

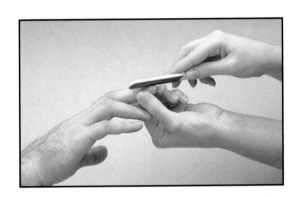

Using side-to-side motions, buff the nail with the black part of the 3-way buffer to smooth out deep ridges in the nail plate. Buff near the cuticle and along the nail grooves, but be careful not to damage the sensitive skin surrounding the nail.

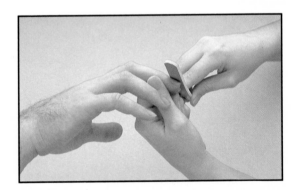

3

Using the white part of the 3-way buffer, continue buffing side to side. The softer white grit smoothes the nail's surface.

4

To bring the nails to a high shine, use the smooth, gray side of the 3-way buffer. Vigorously buff the nail plate until the desired amount of shine has been achieved.

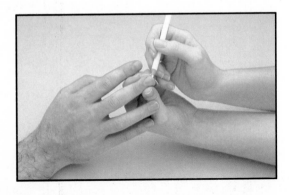

5

To whiten the tip of the nail, use a moistened white stick and rub it gently on the underside of the nail's free edge. Note: The extensive buffing used in this technique removes a layer of the nail. This procedure should be done only every 3 weeks. If additional shine is desired during the interim, apply a coat of clear polish.

HOT-OIL MANICURE

The hot-oil manicure is the perfect solution to dry, chapped skin. This soothing procedure will remoisturize your hands, making them soft and beautiful again.

Follow the steps of the basic manicure, but replace the water that is used during the soaking step with a warm, soothing creme. The creme is heated in a hot-oil machine, which prevents the product from being overheated.

MATERIALS NEEDED:

All items from the basic manicure, page 17
Hot-oil creme
Hot-oil manicure machine

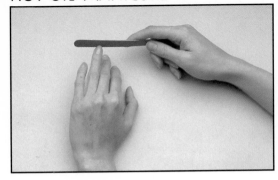

1

Perform steps 1 through 4 of the basic manicure, page 18. Here the nails are filed into a round shape, which complements shorter nails. Begin by rounding the corners as in the oval shape. To obtain the round shape, however, continue rounding the free edge as well.

2

To preheat creme, follow hot-oil manicure machine manufacturer's instructions. Soak your hands in the preheated hot-oil creme in the machine for 5 minutes to allow the creme to penetrate the skin and cuticles.

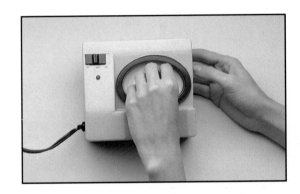

3

Remove your hands and massage the creme into your hands and forearms.

4

Using an orangewood stick with cotton wrapped around the tip, gently push back your cuticles.

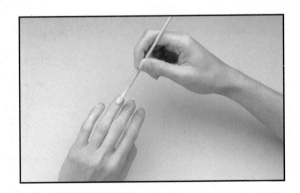

5

Use a cotton-wrapped orangewood stick to remove the creme from underneath your nails. However, be careful not to poke the delicate nail bed with the orangewood stick. Replace the cotton as needed when it becomes saturated with creme. Perform steps 8 through 15 of the basic manicure to complete your manicure.

SILK WRAP

For weak nails, silk wrapping adds the strength necessary to keep nails beautiful. And no matter how perfect the paint job is, the overall effect of your manicure will be ruined if some nails are long and some are short.

Strips of real silk are glued to the top of the nail plate and buffed to a smooth finish to keep your nail's natural look. Silk wrapping is perfect for women who are unable to grow long nails because of weak, soft, brittle nails or nails that break easily. It gives your natural nails extra support, giving them a chance to grow longer under the protection that silk provides. For especially weak nails, a heavier material such as linen may be used instead of silk for extra support.

MATERIALS NEEDED:

All items from the basic manicure, page 17
Silk or linen
Nail glue
Manicure scissors
3-way buffer
Ridge filler

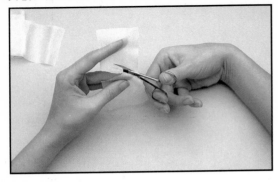

1

Perform steps 1 through 3 of the basic manicure, page 18. Cut the silk to the shape of your nail.

2

Lay the cut silk on your nail to determine if it fits properly. The silk should be at least $\frac{1}{16}$ inch away from the nail grooves and cuticle and should extend over the free edge for about 1 inch. If the piece is too large, continue to trim and measure it until it fits correctly. If it is too small, cut a new piece.

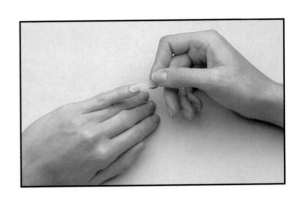

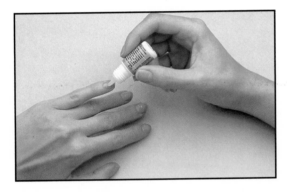

3

Apply nail glue to the center of the natural nail plate and to the tip of the free edge. Use the tip of the glue bottle to spread the glue over the nail. It is important that the glue not reach within $\frac{1}{16}$ inch of the nail grooves or cuticle.

4

Place the cut silk over the glue on the nail plate with the extra inch extending over the free edge. Pull this extra length downward so that it sticks to the tip of the free edge for added strength. Let the glue dry thoroughly.

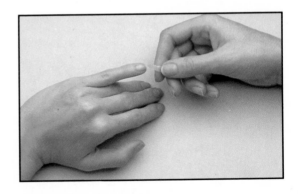

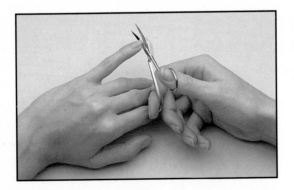

5

Using your manicure scissors, trim the excess silk from the free edge.

6

Using the black portion of the 3-way buffer, file the tip of the free edge smooth.

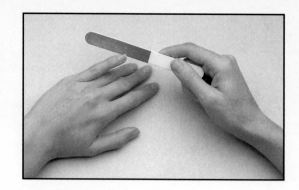

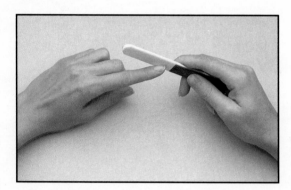

7

Then buff the top of the nail plate to remove the ridges of the silk. Switch to the white grit and continue buffing until the surface is smooth. Since the silk is a thin material, however, be careful not to buff it off entirely.

8

Perform steps 4 through 8 of the basic manicure. Instead of a base coat, ridge filler is applied over silk wraps. Ridge filler helps to even out any unfelt ridges or bumps caused by the silk.

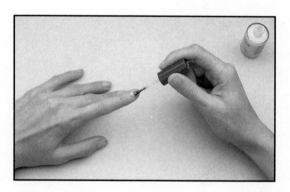

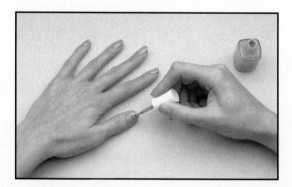

9

To finish your manicure, perform steps 10 through 15 of the basic manicure. As your nail grows, the silk moves forward also. When the silk is halfway down your natural nail, apply another layer over the entire nail. To maintain your silk, use a nonacetone polish remover. To remove silk, soak your nails in acetone polish remover until it dissolves away.

MENDING WITH SILK OR LINEN

In addition to strengthening the entire nail, silk or linen can also be used to repair small tears or splits in the natural nail. If your nail tears, simply apply silk to the damaged area to help prevent the nail from breaking completely off. Since you can't predict when a nail will split, silk and glue are good items to carry in your emergency nail kit.

MATERIALS NEEDED:

Polish remover	Tweezers
Cotton	3-way buffer
Emery board	Ridge filler
Silk or linen	Color polish
Manicure scissors	Top coat
Nail glue	Quick-dry

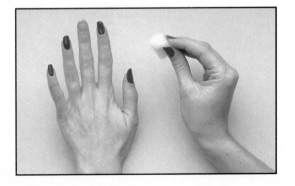

1

Remove the polish from the nail to be mended.

2

Gently file and shape the damaged nail with an emery board.

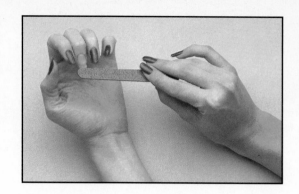

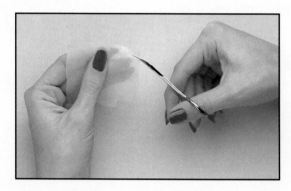

3

Cut and size the silk to the needed shape. If the nail is torn less than halfway across the nail plate, you don't need to cover the entire nail with silk. However, the piece does need to be substantially larger than the tear itself and should cover the surrounding area.

4

Apply the glue to the tear and surrounding areas of the nail.

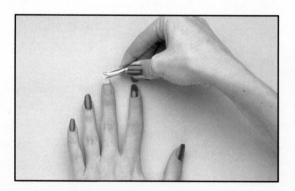

5

Use tweezers to position the silk onto the glue. If the tear is large, you may want to apply more than one layer of silk for extra support.

6

Using all three sides of the 3-way buffer (black to white to gray), smooth the nail's surface. Reapply polish to the nail—ridge filler, two coats of color polish, and top coat. Finish the procedure by applying quick-dry.

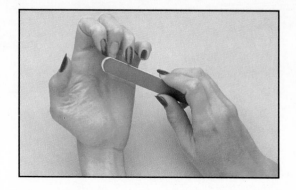

PRESS-ON NAILS

Press-on nails are false fingernails that cover the entire nail plate. They have an adhesive tab to adhere the press-on nail to your natural nail, eliminating the need for glue.

Press-on nails can be purchased in a variety of shapes, sizes, and colors, which saves you time on filing and polishing. This assortment gives you the freedom to change your nail length or color to match your individual needs. These reusable nails make nail designing fun and easy.

MATERIALS NEEDED:

All items from the basic manicure, page 17
Block buffer
Press-on nails in various sizes
Adhesive press-on tabs
Nail file

1

Perform steps 1 through 3 of the basic manicure, page 18. Buff the entire nail plate with a block buffer to remove surface oils.

2

Size the nails to fit the natural shape of your natural nail. The nail should reach to, but not extend past, the cuticle and nail grooves. If the press-on nail is too large, file the sides until it is the correct width.

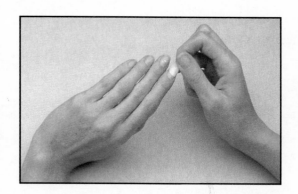

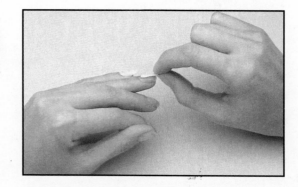

3

Peel the adhesive tab off the waxed paper backing and stick it carefully in the center of the natural nail plate. Rub firmly with an orangewood stick to make sure the adhesive tab is thoroughly attached to the natural nail.

4

Remove the top covering from the adhesive tab.

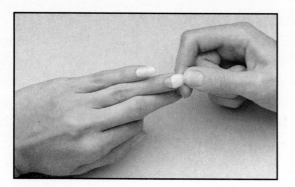

5

Align the press-on nail on top of the adhesive tab and press firmly to remove air bubbles between the natural nail and the press-on nail.

6

File the free edge to the desired length and shape with a nail file.

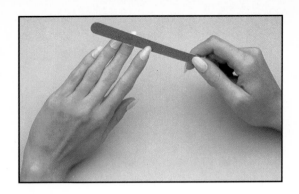

7

Perform steps 9 through 15 of the basic manicure.

TIPS ON TIPS

Nail tips can be purchased in a variety of shapes, sizes, and curvatures. Choosing the tip that best fits your type of nail is crucial to obtaining maximum wearing time. Although nail tips aren't made to last for extended periods of time, they are excellent accessories for special events or as a change of pace and can last up to two weeks.

To size the tips to your fingers correctly, position the well of the nail tip over your natural nail. (The well is the thinner, indented area under the nail tip.) The well should cover only the top half of your natural nail. The sides of the plastic tip should extend from the nail groove on one side to the nail groove on the other. The tip should be as close to the nail grooves as possible, without touching the skin surrounding the nail. If you cannot find a tip that fits exactly, use the next size larger and file both sides of the nail tip until it fits your natural nail.

The various lengths available give you many options for different occasions. Longer lengths are great for more dressy looks, while shorter lengths allow you the freedom to work and carry on everyday tasks easily.

To remove nail tips, fill a glass bowl with acetone polish remover and soak the fingertips for approximately 20 minutes. As the tips soften, they will begin to dissolve. Make sure you leave your fingertips in the polish remover until all traces of the nail tip and glue have disappeared.

NAIL TIPS

When you want your nails to look their best, temporary nail tips can be applied over your natural nails. The tip is glued to the top half of the natural nail and buffed even with the nail plate. You can file the tips into any of the four nail shapes to determine which one you like best. And by experimenting with a variety of polish colors, you can create different looks to match your different moods.

The added length can enhance the look of your hands and draw attention to your new, dramatic look. Adding accessories, such as rings and bracelets, is an excellent way to accentuate your new nail length.

MATERIALS NEEDED:

All items from the basic manicure, page 17
Plastic tips in a variety of sizes
Nail file
Block buffer
Nail glue
Nail clippers
Ridge filler

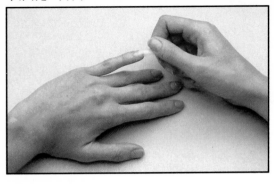

1

Perform steps 1 through 3 of the basic manicure, page 18. Using directions in "Tips on Tips," page 38, size tips to fit all your fingers.

2

Place your file at a 45-degree angle on the end of the tip that attaches to the natural nail. File lightly across this area to thin the edge so it will blend more naturally with your nail. This will reduce the amount of filing you will have to do once the tip is applied.

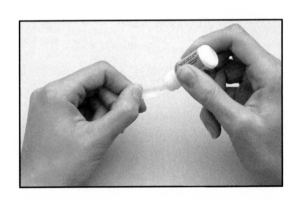

3

With the block buffer, lightly buff the top half of your nail plate. This removes the surface oils and helps improve adhesion.

4

Completely cover the well of the tip (the thinner, indented area) with nail glue.

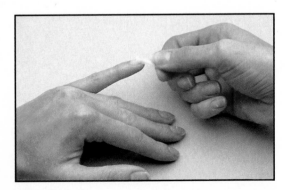

5

Hold the tip at a 45-degree angle against the tip of the free edge.

6

Roll the tip tightly onto the natural nail, making sure no air bubbles appear under the tip. Press the tip firmly against the nail plate for 10 to 15 seconds to allow the glue to dry.

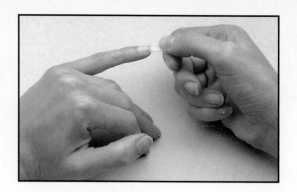

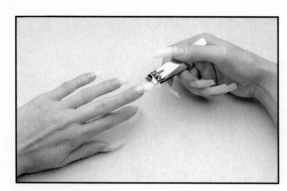

7

Cut and file the free edge to your desired length and shape.

8

Using your nail file, carefully buff the well area flush to your natural nail.

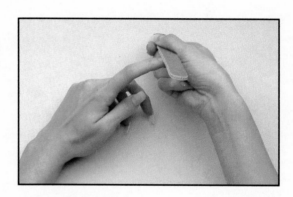

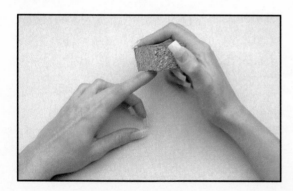

9

With your block buffer, smooth out any additional ridges or bumps.

10

Perform steps 4 through 15 of the basic manicure on pages 18–21, substituting ridge filler for base coat.

PEDICURE

The pedicure is a manicure for the feet. Just as it is important for your hands to be kept well groomed and looking good, your feet need to be cared for. The pedicure is especially flattering in the summer when you frequent the beach and wear sandals. The added time you spend on your feet will pay off when people compliment you on their pretty appearance.

Although a pedicure is similar to the basic manicure, some different procedures and products are used for the grooming of your feet. Because the feet are in shoes all day and support your body weight, they need additional care. Exfoliating the dead skin cells and removing any calluses leave the feet soft and conditioned. Because the bottom of your foot has more than 7,200 nerve endings, a pedicure is one of the most relaxing nail services that can be performed.

MATERIALS NEEDED:

All items from the basic manicure, page 17
Foot bath
Foot antiseptic spray
Nail clippers
Sloughing lotion
Pumice stone or foot file
Foot powder
Toe separators
Slippers

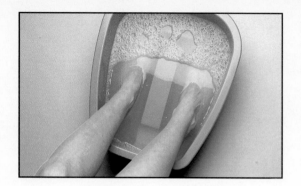

1

Soak the feet in warm, soapy water for 5 minutes.

2

Remove feet and spray with foot antiseptic to reduce germs on the skin. Towel-dry.

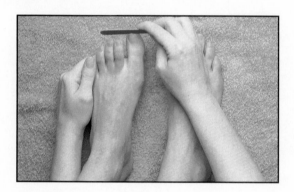

3

Clip and file the nails *straight* across to reduce the chance of developing ingrown toenails.

4

Apply cuticle oil and massage it gently into the skin. Using a cotton-wrapped manicure stick, gently push back the cuticles.

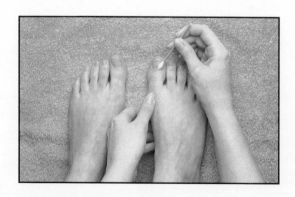

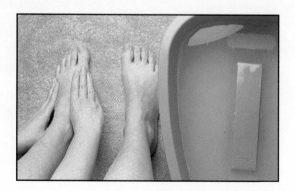

5

Apply sloughing lotion and massage it in until the top layer of skin begins to exfoliate.

6

Return the feet to the foot bath for rinsing and brush them with the plastic nailbrush to remove all traces of dead skin and sloughing lotion.

7

Lightly rub calluses with a pumice stone or foot file. Heavy calluses cannot be removed all at once without causing pain. File them gently during each pedicure to wear them down gradually until they are completely gone.

8

Apply massage creme to the entire foot and shin area to soften and moisturize the skin. Dab foot powder onto the feet with cotton balls to deodorize and help keep the feet from perspiring.

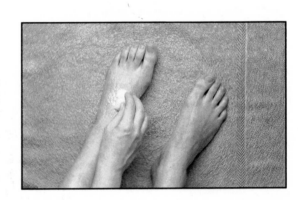

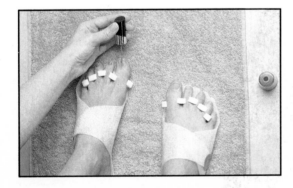

9

Place the toe separators between each toe and put on the paper or plastic slippers to keep the bottoms of your feet clean. Perform steps 8 through 15 from the basic manicure, pages 19–21.

DESIGNING NAIL ART

Nail art gives you the opportunity to let your creativity run wild. What you can design has unlimited possibilities. Nail appliqués such as charms and rhinestones can be purchased in endless shapes and sizes to create a 3-D look. Or ordinary items such as lace or tissue paper can be arranged to form beautiful, unique nail collages.

Even if you think you have limited artistic ability, you can master the easy-to-learn techniques for painting an original creation. Once you've learned these techniques, you can use regular acrylic paints and a fine paintbrush to create an endless variety of designs—on one nail or all ten.

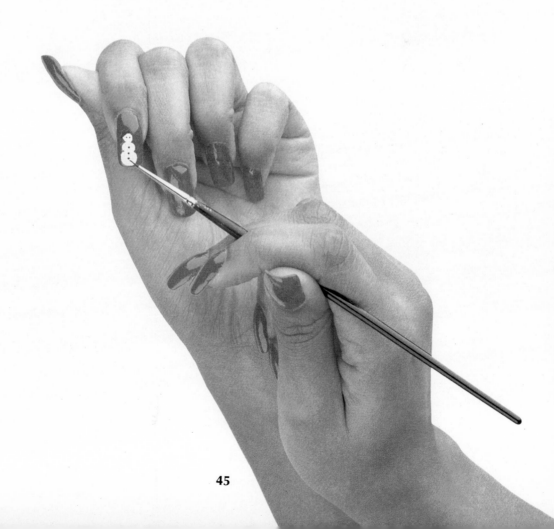

DECALS

MATERIALS NEEDED:

Decals
Scissors
Tweezers
Water
Cuticle scissors
Top coat

46

1

Cut out the desired decal. Grasping the decal with tweezers, dip it into water for 20 to 30 seconds or until it begins to loosen from the backing.

2

Using your fingers, slowly slide the decal off the backing until it is about ¾ of the way off. With the tweezers, grab the edge of the decal and slide it the rest of the way from the backing.

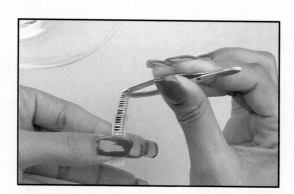

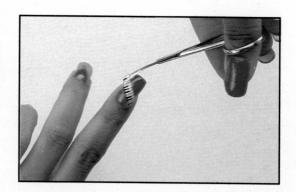

3

Carefully place the decal in your desired position on the dry prepolished nail. Gently smooth the creases with your finger.

4

Trim the edges of the decal to fit within the nail grooves.

5

Brush top coat over the entire nail plate to seal and protect the decal.

RHINESTONE AND CHARM

MATERIALS NEEDED:

Striping tape of your color preference
Manicure scissors
Orangewood stick
Top coat
Water
Rhinestones of your color preference
Tweezers
Nail charm

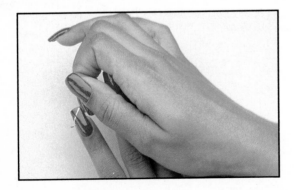

1

Place striping tape diagonally across the top third of your dry prepolished nail. Allow the edges of the striping tape to hang over the nail groove and the free edge.

2

Trim the excess from both ends of the tape with your manicure scissors. The tape should come up to, but not touch, the nail groove and free edge. If necessary use an orangewood stick to flatten the striping tape. Brush top coat on the entire nail plate.

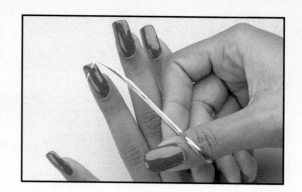

3

Dip the tip of your orangewood stick into water. Use the moistened end to pick up a rhinestone.

4

Set it into place on the wet top coat. Repeat with additional rhinestones.

5

Pick up the nail charm with tweezers and place it onto the wet top coat in the center of the nail. The top of the charm should be positioned toward the cuticle.

6

Once again, brush top coat over the entire nail plate. Apply top coat once a day for the next two days to protect the appliqués.

FLOWERS

MATERIALS NEEDED:

Acrylic paint
Acrylic paintbrush
Water
Top coat

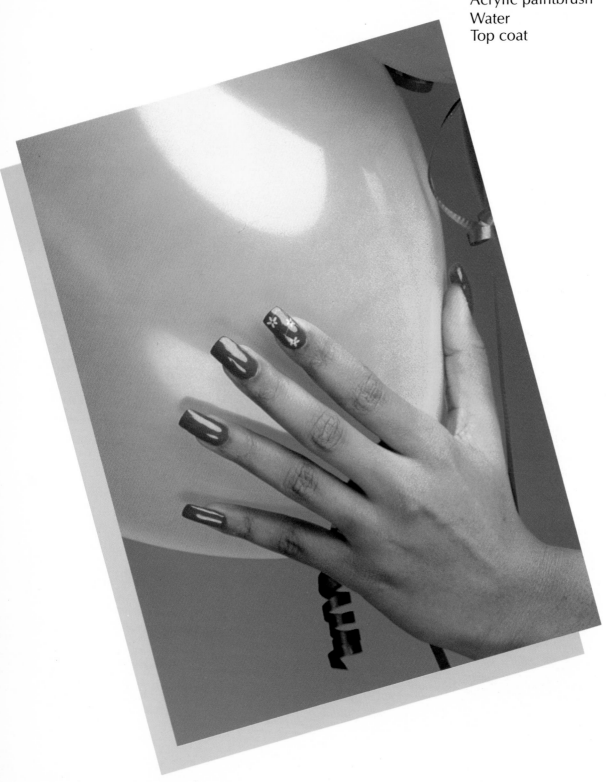

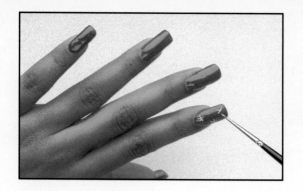

1

Using pink paint, draw 3 small 5-pointed line stars in a triangular pattern on the dry prepolished nail plate.

2

Starting at the center of each star, draw half circles up to the end of each point to form the flower's petals. Fill in the petals.

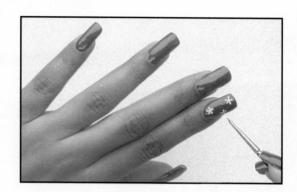

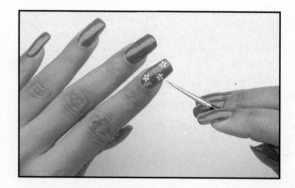

3

Using white paint, apply a dot to the center of each flower.

4

Using dark green paint, lightly draw flower stems and leaves. When all paint is thoroughly dry, apply a top coat over the entire nail plate.

PUPPY
PAW PRINTS

MATERIALS NEEDED:

Acrylic paint
Acrylic paintbrush
Water
Top coat

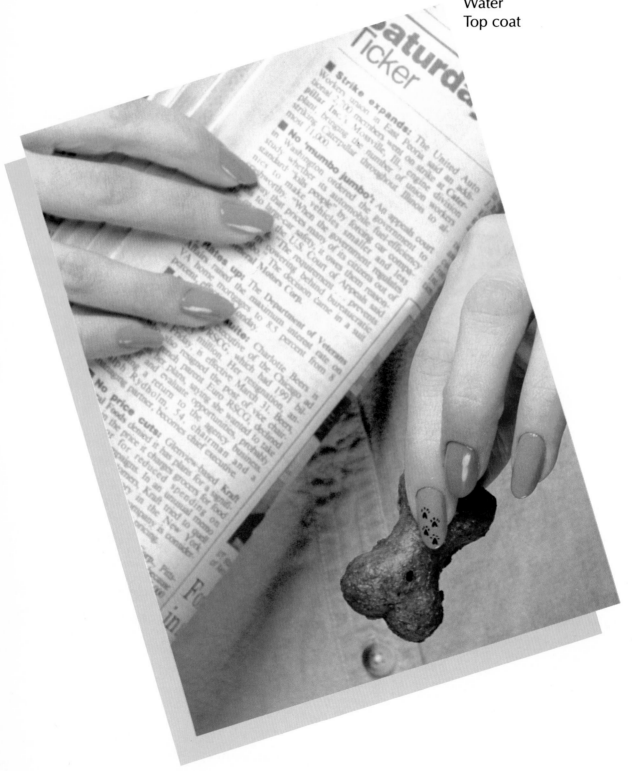

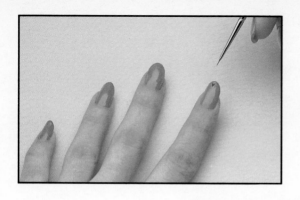

1

With black paint, draw an upside-down heart near the free edge in the center of a dry prepolished nail and fill in.

2

Leave a space and move vertically down the nail, continuing to paint upside-down hearts in a zigzag pattern until you reach the bottom of the nail plate.

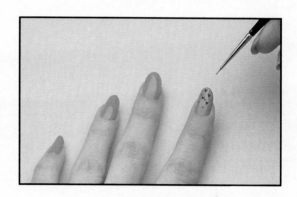

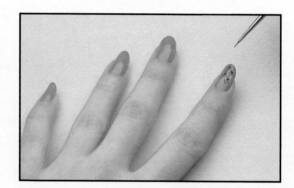

3

Draw four small circles around the point of the heart for the puppy's toe pads. Fill in completely.

4

Repeat the circles at the point of each heart. When all paint is thoroughly dry, apply a top coat over the entire nail plate.

TUXEDO

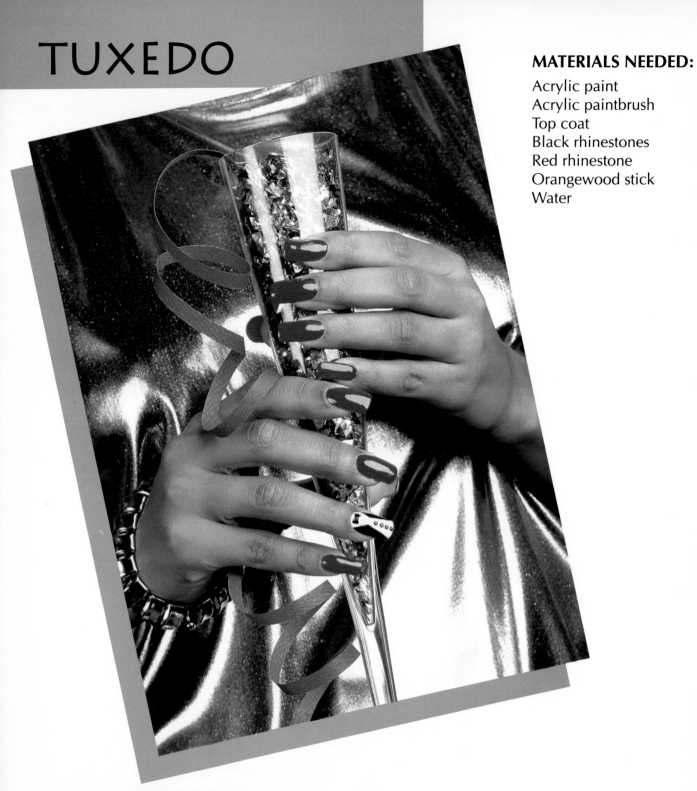

MATERIALS NEEDED:

Acrylic paint
Acrylic paintbrush
Top coat
Black rhinestones
Red rhinestone
Orangewood stick
Water

1

On a white-polished nail, paint an hourglass shape with black paint. Note that the top half of the hourglass is longer than the bottom.

2

Fill in the two resulting triangles on each side of the hourglass with black paint.

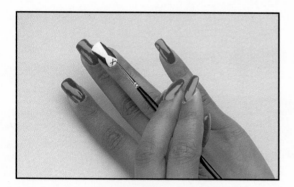

3

Draw a small X with black paint close to the cuticle. Connect the ends of the X to form the bow tie.

4

Fill the X in completely with black paint. Allow black paint to dry thoroughly.

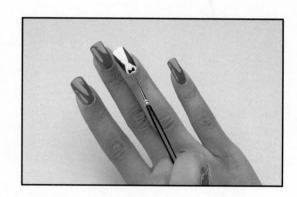

5

Top-coat the top half of the nail plate. Using a moistened orangewood stick, place the three black rhinestones in a vertical line on the nail to form the tuxedo's buttons. If desired, instead of applying the top coat and rhinestones, paint the three buttons with black paint.

6

Apply a dot of top coat in the center of the bow tie and place the red rhinestone onto it. When all paint is thoroughly dry, apply a top coat over the entire nail plate.

PALM TREE

MATERIALS NEEDED:

Acrylic paint
Acrylic paintbrush
Water
Top coat

1

To draw the palm tree's trunk, start in the center of a dry prepolished nail a third of the way down from the tip of the free edge. Draw horizontal comma-shaped lines with brown paint on a slight diagonal, with the commas getting progressively smaller. Stop a third of the way from the cuticle.

2

On the third of the nail close to the cuticle, use green paint to draw horizontal comma-shaped lines on either side of the top of the tree's trunk to form the palm fronds.

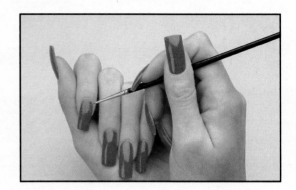

3

In between the brown lines of the trunk, paint white lines to give definition to the trunk.

4

On the third of the nail close to the free edge, use blue paint to draw small squiggly lines for the water.

5

Near the palm tree's fronds, use black paint to draw an elongated M for a sea gull in flight. When all paint is thoroughly dry, apply a top coat over the entire nail plate.

HALLOWEEN MOON AND BAT

MATERIALS NEEDED:

Acrylic paint
Acrylic paintbrush
Water
Top coat

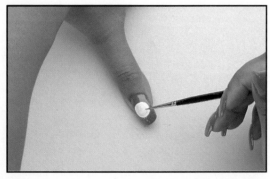

1

Paint a large white circle in the middle of a dry prepolished orange nail. Let dry completely.

2

In the center of the white circle, draw an elongated horizontal M with black paint.

3

Draw a small M in the center of this horizontal line.

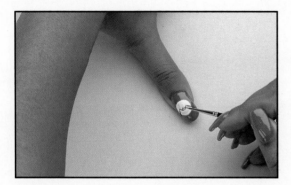

4

Connect the ends of the large M with an inverted V-shaped line to form the bat's outline. Fill in completely.

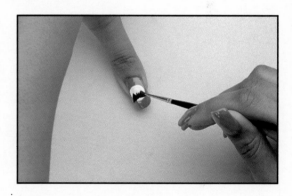

5

For the bat's wings, draw two triangles underneath each side of the inverted V and fill in completely.

6

Draw a small square at the point of the inverted V and fill in completely to form the bat's body. When all paint is thoroughly dry, apply a top coat over the entire nail plate.

DASH OF SPLASH

MATERIALS NEEDED:

Red nail polish
Acrylic paints
Acrylic paintbrush
Silver glitter polish
Water
Top coat

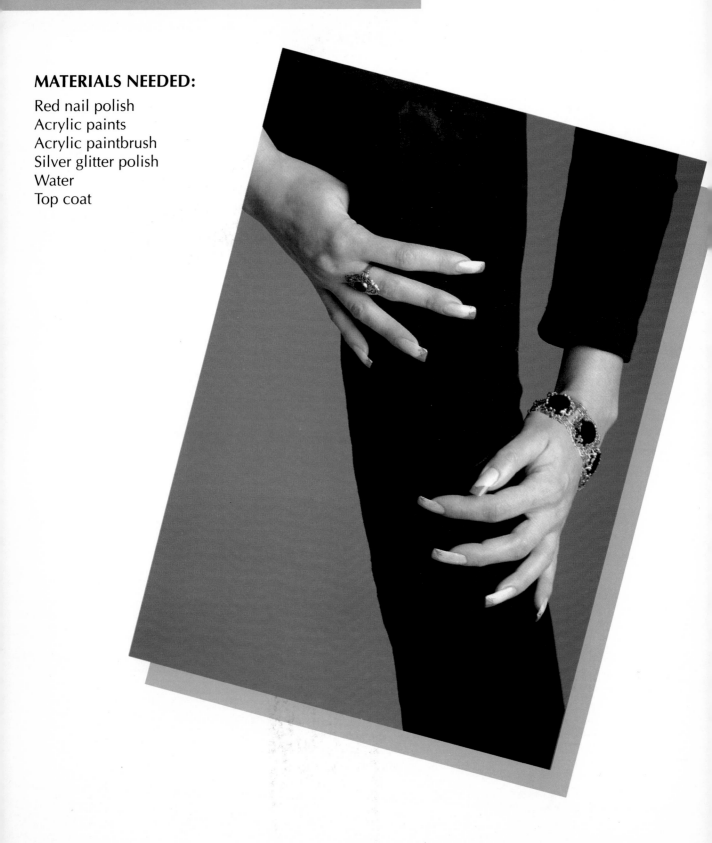

1

On a prepolished opalescent nail, use red nail polish to draw a diagonal line from the edge of the nail groove to the opposite corner of the free edge. Fill in the outlined area completely. Repeat on all ten nails.

2

At the corner of the free edge where the red polish meets the opalescent polish, use dark purple paint to draw a line extending toward the bottom of the nail, branching out in three directions to form wispy stems. Repeat on all ten nails.

3

When the purple paint is dry, apply silver glitter polish lightly over the stems.

4

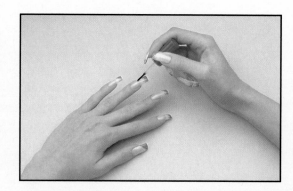

Repeat on all ten nails. When all paint is thoroughly dry, apply top coat.

SNOWMAN

MATERIALS NEEDED:

Acrylic paints
Acrylic paintbrush
Water
Top coat

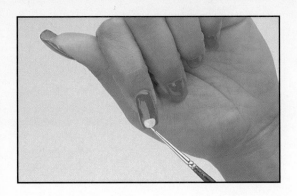

1

In the top half of a dry prepolished nail, use white paint to draw a large circle and fill it in completely.

2

Next to this circle draw a slightly smaller circle and fill in.

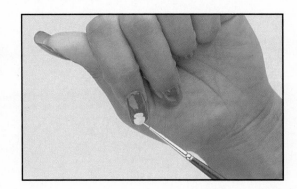

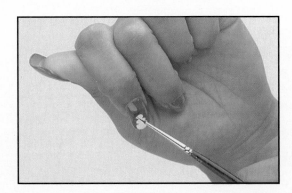

3

Next to the second circle draw another slightly smaller circle and fill in. This completes the snowman's outline.

4

Use black paint to draw a tilted hat on the snowman's head.

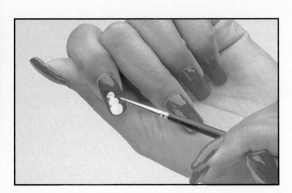

5

Mark two black dots for eyes.

6

Mark three black dots in a vertical line down the center of the two larger circles to form buttons.

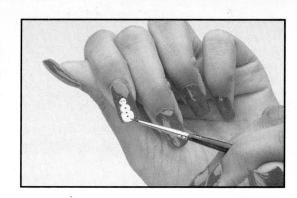

7

Using orange paint, draw a small, elongated sideways triangle below the eyes to form the carrot nose.

8

To form the snowman's scarf blowing in the wind, draw a horizontal line with blue paint, starting at the right side where the smallest circle meets the middle circle. Extend the line on the left side past the snowman's body. At the area extending out to the left, draw a separate line forming a V with the first line. When all paint is thoroughly dry, apply a top coat over the entire nail plate.

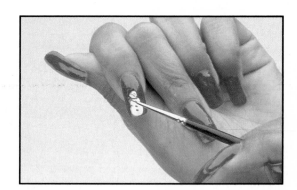